THE DYNAMIC EQUILIBRIUM
OF BODY PROTEINS

*Hemoglobin, Plasma Proteins, Organ
and Tissue Proteins*

THE DYNAMIC EQUILIBRIUM
OF BODY PROTEINS

Hemoglobin, Plasma Proteins, Organ
and Tissue Proteins

By

GEORGE H. WHIPPLE, M.D.

Professor of Pathology Emeritus
Dean of the School of Medicine and Dentistry Emeritus
The University of Rochester
Rochester, New York

CHARLES C THOMAS · PUBLISHER
Springfield · Illinois · U.S.A.

CHARLES C THOMAS · PUBLISHER
BANNERSTONE HOUSE
301-327 EAST LAWRENCE AVENUE, SPRINGFIELD, ILLINOIS, U.S.A.

*Published simultaneously in the British Commonwealth
of Nations by*
BLACKWELL SCIENTIFIC PUBLICATIONS, LTD., OXFORD, ENGLAND

Published simultaneously in Canada by
THE RYERSON PRESS, TORONTO

Printed in the United States of America

CONTENTS

v

THE DYNAMIC EQUILIBRIUM OF BODY PROTEINS

Hemoglobin, Plasma Proteins, Organ and Tissue Proteins

I
Introduction

THE MAIN THEME of this paper is the *dynamic equilibrium* of body proteins. This means that plasma proteins can contribute to the store of intracellular proteins when need arises—that plasma proteins can meet the needs of the body for new proteins. Hemoglobin likewise can contribute effectively to the "protein pool" of the body, but only when it is released from destroyed or obsolescent red cells. Body protein surplus stores likewise can contribute promptly needed plasma proteins. The term body *"protein pool"* suggests that within the total mass of body protein there is a ready interchange between the proteins in circulation, in extracellular fluids, in the cells, and in the reserve stores (Fig. L).

This monograph is not designed to cover all the contributions to this expanding field. A few closely related papers are noted. A considerable number of papers dealing with blood and organ proteins have appeared from this laboratory in the past 30 years. This review attempts an orderly presentation of this material covering the more important experiments and our interpretation of the findings.

3

II
Parenteral Plasma Can Supply All Body Protein Requirements

Experiments published from this laboratory (30) indicate that the normal dog given a protein free diet of fat, carbohydrates, minerals and vitamins can be maintained in nitrogen and weight equilibrium and perfect health by means of adequate dog plasma given intravenously or intraperitoneally over periods of one to three months. The dog receives no significant amount of nitrogen or protein except plasma proteins parenterally which obviously supply all normal body requirements. No surplus of any one of the various plasma proteins appears at any time in the circulating plasma during these long experiments, indicating that all types of proteins under these conditions can be used by the normal body for its maintenance requirements. It is accepted that most of the plasma proteins (albumin, fibrinogen, prothrombin and some other globulins) derive from the liver. The *liver* then is the *master organ* in plasma protein production.

When large amounts of plasma are given to dogs intravenously there develops a degree of *hyperproteinemia* of 9-10 gm. per cent which will be associated with some proteinuria. When plasma injections cease, the proteinuria clears promptly. There is a threshold for plasma proteins in the kidney, but there is no resultant kidney damage in these dogs.

PARENTERAL PLASMA OVER LONG PERIODS

Dog	Parenteral Plasma Duration	N in Plasma Total	N in Diet Total	N in Urine Total	Wt. Loss
	Days	gm.	gm.	gm.	kg.
43-346	92	204	1.0	184	1.2
43-346	76	178	3.0	154	2.0
44-98	76	180	52.0	168	0.2
43-141	32	75	0.2	59	0.6
43-141	52	191	3.9	149	1.3
46-79	15	56	1.8	38	0.0
46-9	16	58	1.9	35	0.1

Table I summarizes the results of seven long experiments in which plasma injections continue during fifteen to ninety-two days. There is very little or no protein in the basal diet. Dogs receive parenterally 2-4 gm. of nitrogen daily as plasma protein in whole normal dog donor plasma. There is a positive nitrogen balance in all experiments. The weight loss is minimal considering the length of the experiments and the clinical condition is excellent.

The methods used in these long experiments are important and have been described (30). Heparin is used as the anticoagulant in collecting blood for transfusion of plasma. Citrate will be toxic and has complicated some experiments in other laboratories. Care in feeding and in the prevention of infection is very important as lack of appetite may terminate an experiment.

III
Globin Conservation

It came as a surprise to us that *globin from hemoglobin* from laked red cells given intravenously or intraperitoneally was utilized in standard dogs to make new hemoglobin and plasma protein. The *dog globin is not used as completely as is plasma protein,* but it is used to form new plasma protein and may even maintain the dog in nitrogen balance. It may be mentioned that the normal 10 kilo dog has a mass of hemoglobin of about 180 gm. and with the life cycle of the red cell as 120 days the dog uses up about 1.5 gm. of hemoglobin per day. Evidently this globin is used in the body economy as is true for the iron, while the pigment radicle is discarded. Elsewhere (22) (Table 2) the experimental data are tabulated to show that in anemic and hypoproteinemic dogs, the dog hemoglobin given parenterally will be conserved and included in the body protein pool.

Hemoglobin is a peculiar basic protein having a low content of some of the essential amino acids (isoleucine and methionine) (3) and it contains a pigment radicle and attached iron. It is generally agreed that iron is conserved in the body but recent studies (8) with radio-iron have emphasized the frugal handling of iron within the body and that *iron absorption* is determined largely by the

TABLE 2

PLASMA AND LAKED RED CELLS INTRAPERITONEALLY—
NITROGEN BALANCE

Dog 43-141 Period No.	Blood Proteins Injected Total N	Total Urinary N	Circulating Plasma Protein Level	R.B.C. Hematocrit	Weight
48 hrs.	gm.	gm.	gm. per cent	vol. per cent	kg.
Basal diet contains little protein (0.86 gm. N per period)					
1		3.31	5.72	41	9.8
2		2.55			
3		2.08			
4		2.34			
Basal diet plus whole blood plasma intraperitoneally					
5	4.60	1.80			9.4
6	4.17	2.53	7.64	38	
7	3.43	1.48			
8	1.86	1.30	8.90	45	9.3
9	3.80	1.61	9.70	40	
10	3.77	2.19			
11	2.07	2.70	9.98	41	9.4
12	3.81	2.52			
13	4.03	2.38			
14	4.06	2.14	9.32	35	9.5
Total......	35.6	20.7			
Basal diet					
15		2.14		29	
16		2.00		30	
17		2.05	7.72	32	
18		1.69			
Basal diet plus laked red blood cells intraperitoneally—globin					
19	4.31	2.00	6.64	36	9.2
20	4.62	2.56	6.61	43	9.2
21	4.10	2.74	6.50	47	
22	1.80	2.40			
23	4.09	2.06			
24	4.30	3.39	6.93	51	
25	2.25	2.46			9.1
26	3.62	3.34		46	
27	3.80	1.86			
28	4.63	2.79			9.1
Total......	37.5	25.6			

need for iron. After hemoglobin destruction the pigment radicle of four pyrrol rings is thrown away in the bile as the body evidently prefers to make new pigment radicles rather than to save the old pigment.

Globin makes up about 95 per cent of the hemoglobin molecule. Its conservation by the body is not well understood, to put it mildly. The experiments given below are concerned with the study of *globin* as it is metabolized in the body. It is clear that under the conditions of these various experiments globin *does contribute effectively* to internal body protein metabolism. Under favorable circumstances the *globin* by parenteral route may maintain the dog in *positive nitrogen balance* for two or three weeks, the globin being the main source of intake nitrogen (Table 2).

Hemoglobin (laked red cells) was given intraperitoneally (Table 2) in about the same amounts as the plasma protein—a total of 37.5 gm. nitrogen during twenty days with a total urinary nitrogen of 25.6 gm. There is a distinct rise in urinary nitrogen of 0.5 gm. per period above control and plasma injection periods. The conservation of globin nitrogen is not as complete as for plasma protein nitrogen but it is surprisingly good in this dog. There is no evidence for rapid and complete breakdown of the introduced globin.

IV

"Raiding" of Body Protein Stores

Reserve stores of body protein can be illustrated by Fig. A. The normal dog is depleted by daily plasmapheresis (bleeding and prompt return of the red cells). Gradually the concentration of plasma proteins falls close to 4 gm. per cent and the basal output of plasma proteins is established for the given basal diet (14). The surplus *reserve* is the amount of protein removed over and above the basal level (Fig. A). In all, this may amount to more protein than the total protein of the liver—obviously the reserve store is not limited to the liver. The reserve varies in different animals and is related to the previous history (diet, exercise, infection).

Reserve stores of protein are found in many organs and tissues, e.g., liver and striated muscle. This reserve can be used for maintenance of these tissues or if certain emergencies arise, for the construction of new red cells and plasma proteins. Body protein reserves can be depleted by continuing demands for new hemoglobin and plasma protein. We have spoken of this reaction as "raiding of body proteins." By continuing anemia and hypoproteinemia with a low protein diet, we re-

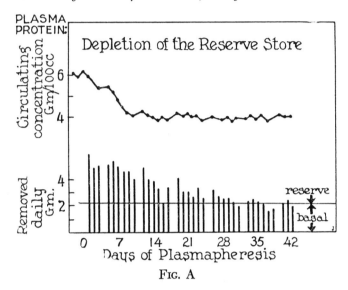

FIG. A

cord large production of hemoglobin and plasma protein with rapid loss of weight even to a fatal termination.

Reserve stores for hemoglobin and plasma protein are indicated in Table 3. Our laboratory normal dogs have high hemoglobin levels and are very active and healthy. They are born and raised in our kennels and accustomed to laboratory procedures. The maximal regenerative capacity is high but does vary somewhat with individual dogs just as their muscular capacity varies. The reserve stores also vary with the individual and its previous dietary and exercise regime.

These reserve stores obviously contribute to the production of new hemoglobin and plasma pro-

TABLE 3
HEMOGLOBIN AND PLASMA PROTEIN IN BODY CIRCULATION AND IN RESERVE STORES

Regenerative capacity of dog

	Circulating Mass	Maximal Regenerative Capacity per week	Reserve Store
	gm.	*gm.*	*gm.*
Hemoglobin	180	50–70	50–200
Plasma Protein	30	50–70+	30–100

Dog 10 kilos=900 cc. blood volume=500 cc. plasma volume.
20 gm. and 6 gm. per cent=normal hemoglobin and plasma protein.

tein when a standard dog is put on a low protein diet and bled regularly (Table 4). The food protein is measured each week as is the removed protein due to bleeding—hemoglobin plus plasma protein.

TABLE 4
DOG 40-33 PROLONGED BLOOD PROTEIN DEPLETION BY BLEEDING

Period	Wt.	Protein Intake Per Wk.	Protein Output				Total Nitrogen Weekly	
			Hemoglobin		Plasma Protein			
			Level	Output Per Wk.	Level	Output Per Wk.	Intake	Urinary Output
1 week	*kg.*	*gm.*	*gm. %*	*gm.*	*gm. %*	*gm.*	*gm.*	*gm.*
1	23.8	0	14.8	98.1	5.1	31.3	—	17.5
2	23.4	19	10.0	43.4	4.4	18.1	3	14.3
3	23.3	19	11.9	20.4	4.3	6.6	3	11.2
4	22.8	19	11.5	42.9	4.3	13.8	3	9.2
5	22.7	18	10.4	18.0	4.0	5.8	2.9	8.3
6	21.5	19	9.2	16.2	4.1	6.1	3	7.5
7	21.4	14	10.4	14.2	4.5	5.4	2.2	7.4
8	20.5	13	10.9	23.6	4.2	7.4	2.1	8.9
9	19.5	12	10.9	2.2	4.1	0	1.9	6.5
Totals........		133		335		95	21.1	90.8

V

Reserve Stores Contribute to Blood Proteins

T HE DOG in Table 4, during a nine-week period, receives 133 gm. of diet protein and produces new hemoglobin 335 gm. plus new plasma protein 95 gm. Obviously the blood proteins must derive from something other than diet protein— that is the *reserve stores* of body protein. There is *no excess protein breakdown* within the body, rather a conservation and decrease in urinary nitrogen week by week. Presumably the new formed blood proteins are formed in their usual organs and tissues by a *modification* of reserve protein with production of the specific plasma and hemoglobin proteins without any extensive cleavage to the amino acid level and subsequent reconstruction. In this emergency, the demand for new blood proteins is predominant and about three times as much hemoglobin is formed as compared with the plasma protein (37).

Premortal rise in urinary nitrogen in long term fasting experiments is accepted in textbooks (1) and frequently mentioned in the literature. It is recorded as due to "greater use of body protein for energy." When the arguments for the use of the term "premortal rise" are reviewed, they are none too convincing. A good review is given by Howe and Hawk (9) but some of the best long term fasting experiments (117 days' fast in a dog with recovery—Howe, Mattill, and Hawk (10)) show no evidence whatever of anything like a "premortal rise." Evidently it is not uniformly observed.

Our experiments tabulated above are not pure fasting experiments but the drain on body protein is very severe and one might expect a "premortal rise" in urinary nitrogen toward the end of these experiments on doubly depleted dogs on a very low protein diet. If there is any tendency for the body to use and break down protein for energy or other purposes, these experiments should favor such a state. It is clear that the body protein is used without any wastage or increase of urinary nitrogen as would be noted if the body protein in excess of normal was broken down before transfer and use.

VI

Premortal Rise in Urinary Nitrogen $=$ Infection

W E VENTURE to suggest a *terminal infection* as a probable explanation of some of the observations associated with a "premortal rise" of urinary nitrogen at the end of long depletion experiments. These animals depleted by low protein diet or otherwise, show depleted reserves of plasma proteins and are surely wide open to a variety of infections. Given an infection, the amount of excess urinary nitrogen would be determined by the severity of the infection and modified by the magnitude of the protein reserve stores. Depleted stores mean decreased output of urinary nitrogen related to any injury as compared with the normal dog with normal reserve stores (6, 13, 32, 35). In spite of severe depletion of stores, a pneumonia would cause significant increase in urinary nitrogen.

Infection in such a dog may sweep through the system as a septicemia or appear as an interstitial pneumonia, and at autopsy could readily be overlooked (Table 5). We suggest that to exclude this possibility and establish a "premortal rise of urinary nitrogen," careful autopsy examination, cul-

TABLE 5

PROLONGED BLOOD PROTEIN DEPLETION—DEATH FROM PNEUMONIA

Dog 43-400					Protein Output			
Period	Weight	Protein Intake		Food Consumption	Hemoglobin		Plasma Protein	
		Type	Weekly		Level	Output Per Week	Level	Output Per Week
1 wk.	*kg.*		*gm.*	*per cent*	*gm. per cent*	*gm.*	*gm. per cent*	*gm.*
1	21.8	Basal & squash	33	95	13.5	98.3	4.9	26.0
2	20.9	Basal & squash	29	82	11.8	52.3	4.4	17.9
3	20.0	Basal & salmon 75	28	81	11.0	37.5	4.6	11.7
4	19.3	Basal & salmon 75	120	87	11.0	35.8	4.5	12.0
5	—	Basal & salmon 75	114	91	8.0	33.5	5.2	15.4
6	17.6	Basal & salmon 40	83	80	8.0	39.6	5.0	23.4
7	16.8	Basal & squash	47	94	8.2	42.4	4.7	23.2
8	16.0	Basal & squash	38	80	6.5	33.0	4.2	17.2
9	15.2	Basal & squash	23	77	6.5	1.3	4.1	0
10	13.6	Basal & squash	17	79	7.3	19.9	4.2	10.5
11	12.9	Basal & squash	15	65	7.3	1.5	3.9	0
Totals............			547			395		157

ture of organs and study of histological sections are essential.

Table 5 (dog 43-400) shows the longest double depletion (bleeding) experiment (eleven weeks), the largest total per cent weight loss (41 per cent or 3.7 per cent per week), and a production of 62 gm. blood protein per kilo weight loss. Rather more protein than usual was contained in the low protein diet (periods 3 to 6) to improve food ingestion (salmon and squash) but the weekly protein intake was quite low. Death occurred four days after termination of the experiment in spite of abundant food intake during these four days.

Autopsy showed an interstitial *pneumonia* which is all too frequent in this type of experiment and may cause death within two or three days. If this interstitial pneumonia had developed a week or so earlier in a less acute form there would have been a considerable increase in urinary nitrogen in the week or so preceding death. It is easy to overlook this type of pneumonia as the lungs in gross are not conspicuously abnormal— in fact, in this very case (Table 5) the lungs were passed in gross as normal.

VII
Phlorhizin Diabetes and Plasma Protein Metabolism

TABLE 6 (dog 35-13) (11) illustrates the results obtained from both the feeding and injection of plasma protein. As soon as the dog had been made *diabetic by phlorhizin,* a twelve hour basal period collection was made and analysis performed. At the beginning of the next collection period the dog was given 302 cc. of dog plasma by stomach tube. This plasma contained 3.36 gm. of nitrogen, 20.84 gm. of protein, and 0.25 gm. of sugar. At the end of this period 1.97 gm. of extra nitrogen and 9.48 gm. of extra sugar were present in the urine above the control basal level. The extra nitrogen amounts to 58 per cent of the fed nitrogen. On the basis of this extra nitrogen one would expect an increase of 7.2 gm. of sugar, whereas 9.48 gm. were recovered. Accompanying the presence of the excess sugar the acetone bodies of both blood and urine drop markedly. These data show that *plasma protein when fed* to the phlorhizinized dog is digested and partially converted into sugar just as are other proteins.

17

Since the D:N ratio had returned to 3.6 at the end of the subsequent basal period, 278 cc. of dog *plasma* were *injected* into the jugular *vein* at the beginning of the next period. It contained 3.08 gm. of nitrogen, 19.00 gm. of protein, and 0.26 gm. of sugar. In the urine collected at the end of

TABLE 6

PHLORHIZINIZED DOG PLASMA BY STOMACH AND BY VEIN

Dog 35-13 Period No.	Urine			Acetone Bodies		Plasma Protein	Plasma Volume	D:N Ratio
	Total N	Urea N NH$_3$-N	Sugar	Blood	Urine			
12 Hours	gm.	per cent	gm.	mg. per cent	gm.	gm. per cent	cc.	
1						6.14	705	
2	5.82	60	22.03	103	2.95	5.27		3.78

Plasma by stomach tube 302 cc. =3.36 gm. N =20.84 gm. protein

3	7.79	83	31.76	50	0.90	4.99		4.08
4	5.13	77	18.47	69	1.25	5.39	6.41	3.60

Plasma by vein 278 cc. =3.08 gm. N =19.0 gm. protein

5	4.96	76	19.77	49	0.86	5.57		3.98
6	4.47	84	19.01	58	0.72	6.01		4.26
7	3.31	76	17.18	67	0.40	5.82		5.19
8	3.73	87	15.15	46	0.26	6.12	638	4.06

this period there was *no excess nitrogen or sugar*. In subsequent basal periods the total excreted nitrogen decreased and the sugar diminished slightly.

When phlorhizinized dogs are fed plasma protein, it is digested with conversion of part of it to sugar. Ketosis decreases as the result of the sugar formation (Table 6) but when phlorhizinized dogs receive *plasma protein by vein,* the injected protein promptly disappears from the blood stream. No protein is lost and there is no excess elimination of nitrogen or sugar in the urine. There is some decrease in the ketosis following injection of plasma protein and the dogs are clinically improved. There is evidence of nitrogen conservation by the body following the parenteral injection of plasma protein. The *metabolism of plasma protein* when fed obviously is different than when it is given (as plasma) parenterally.

We believe that these experiments with phlorhizinized dogs give strong support to the proposal that plasma proteins may gain entrance to body cells and there contribute to the reserve stores and the intracellular metabolism. We believe this goes on without protein breakdown but within the cell these proteins may well be modified and reconstituted from large aggregates.

VIII
The Dynamic Equilibrium of Body Proteins

Further information about the *dynamic equilibrium of body proteins* is obtained by experiments using *radio carbon labeled lysine.* Donor dogs are fed this labeled lysine which is incorporated in the protein molecule and labels the plasma proteins. The labeled plasma proteins as whole plasma removed by bleeding are then given parenterally to standard dogs. This labeled plasma protein disappears from the circulating plasma rather slowly, about one third remaining after six to seven days and appears in the body organs and tissues in corresponding amounts (70-80 per cent, Table 8). There is very little loss of C^{14} as $C^{14}O_2$ in the respired air and less in the urine. The turnover of globulins is more rapid than for albumin within the circulating plasma.

The paper dealing with radio carbon lysine (19) gives many technical details and methods which are very important in this type of experiment. Various related papers in the general literature of this subject (28) are mentioned in that discussion and do not call for further review at this time. The second paper using plasma proteins labeled with Carbon[14] lysine gives important experimental charts and tables to show the fluid equilibrium be-

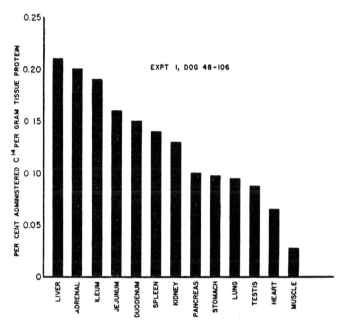

Fig. B. Dog 48-106, Experiment I. Relative C^{14} activity of blood-free tissues forty-nine hours after intravenous injection of C^{14}-labeled plasma. The values shown include extravascular fluid protein activity.

tween plasma proteins and tissue proteins (41).

Figure B shows the relative concentration of C^{14} within the organs at the end of *forty-nine hours* following intravenous injection of labeled plasma—the figures are in per cent administered C^{14} per gram of *organ or tissue protein*. Figure C shows the same values after *seven days* following intravenous injection of labeled C^{14} plasma protein. The highest concentrations are noted in

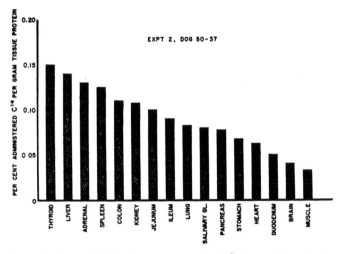

Fig. C. Dog 50-37, Experiment 2. Relative C^{14} activity of blood-free tissues seven days after intravenous injection of C^{14}-labeled plasma. Extravascular fluid protein activity is included.

liver, adrenal and thyroid; medium values for the intestinal tract, spleen, and kidney; lower values for pancreas, salivary glands and lungs; low values for striated muscle and skin. Larger *total amounts* of C^{14} because of tissue weight are found in the muscles 21-28 per cent of total intake, in the skin 12-13 per cent and liver 7-8 per cent (Table 7).

Table 7 shows the concentration figures of C^{14} in the various organs and tissues. After intravenous injection of labeled plasma protein, the distribution is given forty-nine hours later (dog 48-106) and seven days later (dogs 50-37 and

TABLE 7

TOTAL C^{14} TISSUE RECOVERY AFTER INTRAVENOUS
INJECTION OF LABELED PLASMA

Source of C^{14}	Per Cent Administered C^{14}		
	Dog 48-106 (49 Hrs.)	Dog 50-37 (7 Days)	Dog 49-131 (7 Days)
Heart.................	0.64	0.73	0.69
Lungs.................	0.88	0.68	1.12
Spleen.................	0.25	0.32	0.78
Stomach...............	1.82	0.85	1.14
Duodenum..............	0.60	0.31	0.36
Jejunum...............	1.57	0.66	1.11
Ileum.................	2.36	1.47	1.80
Colon.................		0.50	0.61
Pancreas..............	0.12	0.19	0.22
Liver.................	7.62	7.20	7.05
Adrenals..............	0.06	0.03	0.02
Kidneys...............	0.85	0.56	0.79
Salivary glands...........		0.07	0.12
Thyroid...............		0.04	
Skeletal muscle...........	21.90	22.60	28.75
Skin.................		13.80	12.60
Brain.................		0.28	0.21
Uterus................			0.18
Testes................	0.10		
Fat.................		2.45	4.10
Total.................	38.77	52.74	61.65

49-131, Table 7). These figures include some of the extravascular fluid protein.

Table 8 shows *total figures of C^{14}* contained in various tissues, body fluids, expired air and urine. Small amounts of $C^{14}O_2$ appear in the *respired air* (about 2.5 per cent of the total C^{14} given in plasma protein). The figures for expired $C^{14}O_2$ in Table 8 noted as 5-6.7 per cent contain probably about 2-3 per cent derived from residual non-protein C^{14} remaining in the whole donor plasma. Small amounts of C^{14} appear in the *urine* and traces in the *feces*.

TABLE 8

TOTAL C^{14} RECOVERY AFTER INTRAVENOUS INJECTION
OF LABELED PLASMA PROTEIN

Source of C^{14}	Experiment 1	Experiment 2	Experiment 3
	Dog 48-106 49 Hours	Dog 50-37 7 Days	Dog 49-131 7 Days
	Per Cent Administered C^{14}		
Tissues.....................	38.77**	52.74	61.65
Plasma and perfusate.........	34.50	16.00	16.70
Plasma removed in sampling...	5.80	5.60	7.90
Expired CO_2................	5.20	6.73	4.92
Urine......................	0.50	2.50	1.31
Red blood cells..............	Trace	4.00	4.33
Total Recovery...........	84.77	87.57	96.81

** Brain, bone marrow, skeleton, integument, colon, lymphoid, and areolar tissues not sampled.

IX
C¹⁴ Found in Lysine of Plasma and Liver Proteins

L‍YSINE DERIVED from *plasma* and *liver* contained practically all the radio C^{14} activity. The four amino acids, lysine, glutamic acid, aspartic acid, and arginine, were separated from *hydrolysates of plasma and liver protein* from each of the three dogs (Tables 7 and 8). The plasma proteins were precipitated from the fluid removed at the time of viviperfusion. In each instance, the specific activities of *glutamic* and *aspartic acid* derived from plasma protein were less than 1 per cent of the specific activity of *lysine* from the same source while no significant activity was detected in any of the plasma *arginine* samples. Of the four amino acids isolated from liver protein only lysine contained measurable C^{14} activity.

X
C¹⁴ Plasma Protein Fed

A great contrast in the *distribution* of C^{14} is seen when a comparison is made between *oral and intravenous administration* of lysine labeled plasma protein in the dog. After *labeled plasma feeding*, incorporation of the label into the plasma proteins of the recipient occurs *rapidly* but the maximum, attained between seven and ten hours, is *only 6-8 per cent* of the activity fed. Contrast this amount with the figures given in Table 8 where large amounts of C^{14} (70-80 per cent) are found in tissues and body fluids following *intravenous* injection of C^{14} plasma protein. Large amounts of $C^{14}O_2$ appear in the respired air (16-28 per cent of fed C^{14} within forty-eight hours). This is to be compared with 5-6 per cent of C^{14} given by vein which is found in the respired air (Table 8). When C^{14} lysine included in an amino acid digest is fed to dogs the picture is precisely the same as with fed labeled plasma protein (43).

TABLE 9

C¹⁴ ACTIVITY IN CIRCULATING PLASMA AFTER FEEDING LABELED PLASMA
FIGURES GIVE PER CENT OF TOTAL C¹⁴ FED

Sample	Dog 51-137		Dog 49-23		Dog 48-222		Dog 50-176		Dog 43-141	
Time After Feeding	Total Plasma	Non-protein	Total Plasma	Non-protein	Total Plasma	Non-protein	Total Plasma	Non-protein	Total Plasma	Non-protein
45 min.	—	—	2.86	—	1.39	93	—	—	3.35	84
2½ hrs.	5.3	26	—	—	4.15	59	3.60	65	5.70	35
4½ hrs.	7.5	20	6.55	0	4.82	13	6.12	45	6.97	7
7 hrs.	—		7.72	0	5.77	—	—		7.62	0
10 hrs.	8.0	0	7.61	0	5.96	4	6.67	7	7.80	0
24 hrs.	7.4	0	7.52	0	5.45	0	5.67	0	7.02	0
48 hrs.	6.4	—	5.76	0	4.60	0	4.47	0	5.67	0
72 hrs.	—	—	5.40	0	3.33	0	3.90	0	4.75	0
96 hrs.	4.5	0							Digest plus C¹⁴ lysine	

XI

C^{14} Escapes as $C^{14}O_2$ in Respired Air

THE MOST important *excretory pathway* of C^{14} after giving labeled plasma protein by mouth or by vein is *through the lungs* (Table 10). After oral administration 16-28 per cent of the label has been recovered as $C^{14}O_2$ in forty-eight hours with about 80 per cent of this total excreted during the first twelve hours (Table 10). Since variations in total $C^{14}O_2$ excretion, due entirely to differences occurring within the first seven hours, are not related to the amount of C^{14} incorporated into plasma proteins, they probably reflect different degrees of uptake of C^{14} by the tissues during the early stages of the experiment (Table 9). Intravenous injection of lysine-ε-C^{14} labeled plasma proteins in dogs results in a much smaller loss of activity in expired air. If the variable initial peaks, attributed to residual non-protein C^{14} in the donor plasma, are excluded, the rates of $C^{14}O_2$ excretion decline gradually from maxima of about 0.1 per cent of the dose per hour and in a two-day period approximately 2.5 per cent of the in-

28

jected activity is eliminated in this manner (Table 8) (43).

Relatively small amounts of activity appear in the *urine* of these dogs irrespective of the route

TABLE 10

CUMULATIVE TOTAL C^{14} EXCRETED AS CARBON DIOXIDE THROUGH LUNGS PER CENT DOSE FED

Dog No.	0–2 Hrs.	0–7 Hrs.	0–12 Hrs.	0–24 Hrs.	0–48 Hrs.
51-137	6.2	17.6	20.6	23.2	25.3
49-23	5.0	15.6	17.2	18.9	20.8
48-222	4.1	20.9	23.1	25.4	27.9
20-176	2.6	9.8	11.7	13.8	15.8
43-141	6.1	13.6	15.2	16.8	18.8

of administration of lysine-labeled plasma. An average forty-eight hour urinary C^{14} excretion of 1.7 per cent after plasma feeding and one of 1.0 per cent or less after intravenous injection (43) have been found in this laboratory (Table 8). The *feces* contain only traces of C^{14}.

XII

The Placenta Is Very Active in Protein Metabolism

Recent experiments indicated below give clear evidence that the placenta is indeed an important organ in protein metabolism of the mother and fetus. The placental parenchyma (the trophoblastic chorionic epithelium) is a very active tissue in protein metabolism. In fact, the placental epithelium gram for gram is probably two or three times as active as the hepatic epithelium of the mother.

It is well known that certain antibody proteins may pass the placental barrier between maternal and fetal blood in some species, and interest in the broad problem of plasma protein transfer across the placenta has centered almost exclusively on its immunologic aspects (2, 4, 12). It has been shown that the placentas of human beings, rabbits, and guinea pigs readily permit the passage of antibodies from mother to fetus, whereas the placentas of dogs, horses, sheep, goats and pigs are impermeable to the passage of these proteins.

The placenta is the most interesting and prob-

ably the least understood of the various maternal
and fetal tissues included in this study. The placenta in mid and late term development consists
essentially of maternal venous sinuses into which

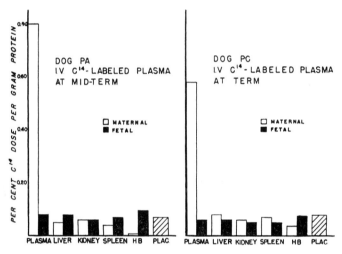

Fig. D. *Intravenous* labeled plasma at *mid term*—dog
PA killed two days later. Comparison of plasma and
organ C^{14} concentration placenta values given. Also dog
PC at *full term* given labeled plasma and killed three
days later. Note *placenta*.

dip the chorionic villi carrying the fetal vessels.
The maternal and fetal bloods are separated by
the *trophoblastic chorionic epithelium—the essential parenchyma of the placenta*—and a variable
amount of connective tissue stroma and capillary
endothelium. In actual bulk, when compared with

the rest of the placenta, the chorionic epithelium probably does not exceed 40 per cent.

Until quite recently the placenta was considered to function as a semi-permeable membrane and when anything was observed which could not be explained by the function of such

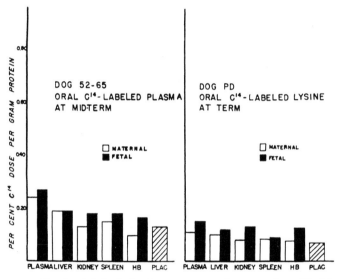

Fig. E. *Oral* labeled plasma at mid term dog 52-65. Killed four days later. Plasma, organ and placenta concentration. Dog PD at term fed labeled lysine and killed four days later—note fetal and placental concentration of C^{14}.

a membrane, it was concluded that breaks or epithelial injury in the villi was responsible. Recent evidence indicates that the placenta does permit passage of proteins, for example, antibodies, in certain species (12) and it probably elaborates some specific hormones.

The assumption that the *placenta is an organ* with other tasks besides the obvious is supported by much evidence (40) and the observations on dogs described in this paper (34) give very specific evidence that it is concerned with *protein metabolism of the mother and fetus.*

After introduction of *labeled proteins into the maternal circulation,* C^{14}-labeled proteins appear in fetal plasma and organs (Fig. D). This, it is believed, must be related to the great activity of the placental parenchymal epithelium which accepts and possibly modifies the labeled plasma protein before passing it to the fetus.

The behavior of *fed* C^{14} lysine and *parenteral* plasma proteins labeled with C^{14} lysine are different. As in the normal dog, so too the pregnant dog given intravenous labeled plasma shows a sustained high plasma protein concentration with slow passage of the plasma protein into the maternal organs, the placenta and the fetal organs. There is no evidence of any protein breakdown during this time as would be noted in the urinary nitrogen. When labeled plasma or C^{14} lysine is *fed* (Fig. E) we note a more rapid movement of the C^{14} lysine into the various maternal organs, placenta and fetal organs. All this points to the great importance of the placental epithelium in the protein metabolism of the mother and fetus.

XIII
Mechanism of Transfer of C^{14}-Labeled Plasma Protein to Organ Protein

FURTHER DISCUSSION concerns the mechanism of transfer of C^{14} activity from plasma protein to tissue protein. Opinions differ sharply regarding the degree to which plasma proteins must be degraded within the body before they become available to cells and tissues. Within a period of seven days, 30-40 per cent of the C^{14} activity of intravenously injected plasma protein, tagged with radioactive lysine, is incorporated into the tissue and organ proteins of dogs. This conversion is accompanied by the loss in either urine or expired air of only a small fraction of administered C^{14}, even when the excretion of C^{14} activity in the first twelve hours, related to non-protein C^{14} in the injected plasma is taken into consideration.

The activity remains in the *lysine residue of the liver proteins* as demonstrated, and very probably of other organ proteins, and the ratio of lysine activity to total protein activity in liver and plasma is unaltered. The very considerable amount of urinary nitrogen, in terms of protein catabolized, excreted by these dogs in seven days

34

compared with the insignificant quantity of C^{14} in the urine suggests either that this nitrogen is derived from as yet unlabeled protein, from tissue or red cell breakdown, or that the lysine released from plasma and tissue proteins is almost completely conserved as such. In view of the relatively high content of C^{14} in the expired air following *oral feeding of labeled plasma* or tracer doses of 1-lysine added to casein digest, it is difficult to believe that complete breakdown to amino acid level at a rate sufficient to account for the observed transfer of C^{14} from plasma to tissues could occur without a greater degree of C^{14} loss.

It appears that the problem is pushed back *into the cell*—for example the liver cell—in this study of protein equilibrium. There are no known forces *outside the cell* capable of *significant* protein degradation and, or protein construction in the dog. This shift of plasma proteins to cell proteins of various types in various organs—liver, adrenal, muscle, and so on—means production of a great variety of substances of protein nature. At present some workers think that the plasma proteins are degraded on the cell surface or within the cell to amino acids, but one might suggest the possibility of more nitrogen escape in the urine under such assumed conditions. We prefer to think of the cell as effecting this shift of one protein to another by a less drastic cleavage and reassembly; polypeptide size being concerned or cleavage of that order.

XIV
Disease and Protein Metabolism

THE EXPERIMENTS listed above have related to normal dogs. When abnormalities appeared, the dogs were eliminated from the normal series—for example distemper, parasitic infestation, acute or chronic nephritis. We have studied certain conditions which relate to abnormal states, especially abnormalities of the liver. The Eck fistula and bile fistula dogs have been studied in much detail.

XV
Inflammation Decreases the Production of Hemoglobin

INFLAMMATION has been included in this program, for example, chance infections due to bacteria or viruses and sterile abscesses produced by an irritant (turpentine). *Endometritis* may develop in a dog with continuing fever and leucocytosis lasting over weeks (26).

A *sterile abscess* has some advantages for experimental purposes over the abscess due to bacteria. It can be terminated at will by incision. Healing is very prompt, yet the fever, leucocytosis, pus formation, and other abnormalities are identical in both types of abscess. The abscess in the acute stage (three to four days) produces an increase in urinary nitrogen and a decrease in new hemoglobin production in standard anemic dogs.

XVI

Endometritis Decreases Hemoglobin Production

A LONG continued *endometritis* in dogs is responsible for long anemic periods during which liver and iron-rich diets do not raise the hemoglobin production (27). Removal of the infected

TABLE 11

INFECTION—ENDOMETRITIS DECREASES HEMO-
GLOBIN PRODUCTION

Dog 27-240 Diet Periods 1 Wk. Each	Food Consumed	Weight	R.B.C.	Hemo- globin Removed
Food, gm. per day	per cent	kg.	mil.	gm.
Bread 275, salmon 125, Klim 20	89	13.3	4.5	12.1
Bread 275, salmon 150, Klim 20	91	13.5	4.2	2.2
Bread 275, salmon 150, Klim 20	79	12.9	5.6	20.5
Bread 225, salmon 200, Klim 20	85	13.5	4.1	1.2
Pig kidney 300, bread 225	71	12.3	3.9	1.4
Pig kidney 300, bread 225	93	12.6	4.5	11.2
Bread 225, salmon 200, Klim 20	82	12.6	3.8	1.3
Bread 225, salmon 200, Klim 20	95	12.2	3.7	1.8
Bread 200, salmon 200, Klim 20	96	12.0	4.2	1.5

Hysterectomy—Transfusions—Total 42 gm. Hb.

Bread 250, salmon 200, Klim 20	100	11.7	4.2	2.0
Bread 300, salmon 200, Klim 20	100	12.0	5.4	40.5
Bread 300, salmon 200, Klim 20	100	12.0	4.9	27.5
Bread 300, salmon 200, Klim 20	100	12.2	4.5	12.5
Bread 350, salmon 125, Klim 20	100	12.7	4.8	22.9
Bread 350, salmon 125, Klim 20	100	12.7	5.5	46.6
Bread 350, salmon 125, Klim 20	100	13.1	4.8	34.0
Bread 350, salmon 125, Klim 20	100	13.0	4.6	23.7
Bread 350, salmon 125, Klim 20	98	13.2	4.6	14.0
Bread 375, salmon 100, Klim 20	100	13.2		26.4
Bread 375, salmon 100, Klim 20	100	13.3	5.5	34.3

uterus is followed by prompt return to the usual
abundant hemoglobin production in anemia—this
in spite of a diet unfavorable for hemoglobin production. This response we assume indicates that

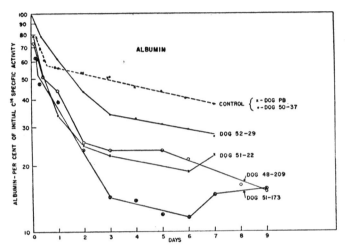

FIG. F. Disappearance curves of C^{14}-labeled albumin
from the plasma of dogs with turpentine abscesses and
normal control dogs after intravenous injection of
labeled plasma proteins.

during the weeks of inflammation the dog did
absorb some of the necessary materials used in
hemoglobin production, but the aggregation of
these products was inhibited by the inflammation.

An example of the effects of endometritis is
shown in Table 11. Dog 27-240 was in normal
condition up to seven to nine weeks preceding the
hysterectomy. There was a little bloodstained

vaginal discharge and leucocytosis August 14. Operation and removal of large uterus August 23. Recovery was uneventful. Transfusions (42 gm. Hb.) were given before and after operation to

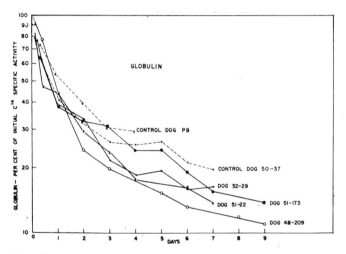

Fig. G. Disappearance curves of C^{14}-labeled globulin from the plasma of dogs with turpentine abscesses and normal control dogs after intravenous injection of labeled plasma proteins.

insure rapid recovery. *Uterus* was enlarged to 2-3 cm. in diameter. The mucosa was purulent. Sections showed acute and chronic *endometritis* —cultures B. coli.

Radio carbon labeled plasma proteins enable the investigator to study the effects of inflammation in more detail. Sterile *abscesses* are used since the abscess reaction can be terminated promptly at any time by incision and drainage. The appearance of C^{14} in new hemoglobin is delayed—evidence of *impaired synthesis* in anemia. The turnover of plasma albumin is greatly accelerated by this sterile inflammation.

Disappearance rates for *albumin* and globulin C^{14} given intravenously are graphically illustrated in Figs. F and G. In the dogs with turpentine abscesses the *albumin activity drops* rapidly for two to three days before reaching the slow steady rate seen after twenty hours in the control dogs. Dog 52-29 with only one abscess showed the least drop and dog 51-173 with two abscesses lost the most weight and showed the greatest decline in albumin C^{14} activity.

XVII
Albumin Reacts to Abscesses

Accelerated albumin turnover is clearly indicated for two to three days in those experiments involving administration of labeled plasma protein by vein. During this time interval, corresponding more or less with the height of the abscess reaction, the *half-life of albumin* is only one and one-half to two days compared with a half-life of about nine days for albumin in normal dogs on the same protein-free diet. This rapid fall in specific C^{14} activity which occurs without any appreciable lowering of total albumin concentration in the plasma indicates an equal increase in the rates of both production and utilization of this plasma protein fraction. In view of these findings it is possible that the low maximum levels of albumin C^{14} activity found after *feeding labeled plasma* or lysine are due to this markedly increased rate of turnover rather than to impaired synthesis. However, diversion of some C^{14}-labeled dietary lysine to fibrinogen with reduced incorporation into albumin cannot be excluded.

The turnover of intravenously injected labeled globulin, on the other hand, appears to be approximately the same in dogs with abscesses and in normal controls (Fig. G). Further evidence that globulin metabolism is relatively unaltered derives from the feeding experiments in which oral C^{14} is incorporated into plasma globulins other than fibrinogen in similar fashion in both abscesses and control animals.

XVIII
Fibrinogen Reaction to Abscesses

Fibrinogen production and turnover are spectacular. When an amino acid mixture with added labeled lysine is fed to these *abscess dogs*, the C^{14} activity incorporated into fibrinogen, gram for gram, is many times greater than for any other circulating protein. This activity also disappears rapidly from circulating fibrinogen and a half-life of two days or less is indicated (Fig. H). Fibrinogen has been known as a very labile protein reacting to acute inflammation usually with two- or even four-fold increases. *Liver injury* (chloroform) *will reduce* the plasma fibrinogen levels within 24 to 48 hours to one-half or even one-fourth of normal (7).

Pus shows a good deal of C^{14} both in cell debris and fluid. As the inflammation continues, the more active organs, e.g., liver, will lose C^{14} but the large stores of C^{14} protein in muscles and skin will then contribute C^{14} to the liver—a dynamic equilibrium.

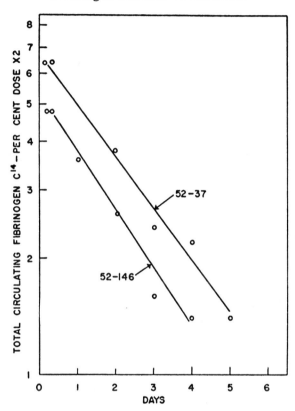

FIG. H. Disappearance rate of total circulating fibrinogen C[14] activity in dogs with turpentine abscesses. Fibrinogen was labeled by feeding.

XIX

Abscess Dogs and C^{14}O$_2$ Expired

THE ESCAPE of C^{14}O$_2$ in the expired air is shown in Table 12. The *abscess* dogs show the escape of more C^{14}O$_2$ than is found in normal control dogs. This holds whether the C^{14} lysine is fed or given as labeled plasma by vein. Presumably this reaction is due in large part to the accelerated turnover of albumin and fibrinogen in the abscess dogs.

TABLE 12

CUMULATIVE TOTAL C^{14}O$_2$ EXCRETION IN EXPIRED
AIR—ABSCESS EXPERIMENTS

Findings After Intravenous C^{14}-Labeled Plasma, Per Cent C^{14} Injected

Dog No.	0–2 Hrs.	0–10 Hrs.	0–24 Hrs.	0–48 Hrs.	0–96 Hrs.	0–end of Experiment
48-209	0.56	1.79	4.50	7.90	12.03	17.83 (9 days)
51-173	0.64	2.35	7.52	13.58	17.66	27.24 (9 days)
52-29	0.90	3.38	5.64	8.32	12.69	16.31 (7 days)
Controls, averages	0.50	1.96	2.91	4.65	7.16	7.7 (7 days)

Findings After Oral C^{14}-Labeled Plasma or C^{14}-Labeled Lysine, Per Cent C^{14} Absorbed

Dog No.	0–2 Hrs.	0–10 Hrs.	0–24 Hrs.	0–48 Hrs.	0–96 Hrs.	0–end of Experiment
51-197 (plasma)	1.25	10.62	16.25	19.80	27.60	30.40 (7 days)
52-97 (plasma)	2.84	11.26	21.13	31.11	35.61	—
52-37 (D, L-lysine)	14.48	38.78	41.93	—	—	—
52-146 (L-lysine)	14.48	28.30	30.40	32.40	35.30	—
Controls, averages	15.00	17.50	21.00	23.00	—	—

XX

Experimental Ascites and Protein Circulation

EXPERIMENTAL ASCITES can be produced in the dog by constriction of the vena cava just above the diaphragm. In considerable measure the degree of constriction will determine the rapidity of accumulation of the ascitic fluid. Sodium will favor and high protein will decrease the production of the ascitic fluid (15).

As the ascitic fluid accumulates, it contains proteins of the type seen in the blood plasma—albumin and globulins but no fibrinogen. Fibrinogen may appear if acute inflammation develops within the peritoneal cavity during an experiment. If this ascitic fluid is removed frequently the body is drained of proteins and there develops a hypoproteinemia with related abnormalities. This may be termed an *internal plasmapheresis* in contrast to the external plasmapheresis consisting of whole blood removal and return of the washed red cells.

The *ascitic protein pool* is a part of the great body protein pool with rapid continuing exchange as shown below (Fig. J). This may be described as a *circulation of ascitic fluid* (16).

It is apparent from published data (17) that

47

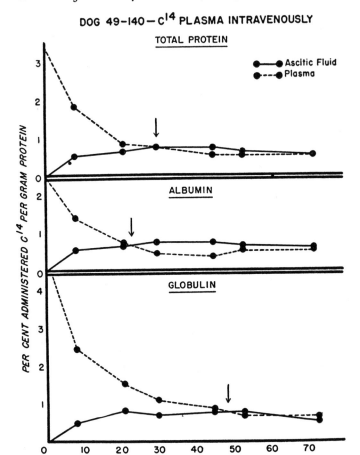

FIG. J. Dog 49-140–Experimental Ascites. Labeled plasma given intravenously. Ascitic fluid level crosses the circulating plasma level.

proteins are constantly passing into and out of both plasma and ascitic fluid under the experimental conditions obtaining, and that following the injection of labeled plasma into either the blood stream or the peritoneal cavity, the rates of protein transfer in opposite directions tend to become equal as the concentrations of tagged proteins in the two compartments approach an even distribution (Fig. K). However, in the early stages of each experiment, when labeled proteins are first appearing and increasing in plasma or ascitic fluid, depending on the site of injection, the flow of labeled proteins will be approximately unidirectional. It is thus possible to estimate minimum relative rates of transfer of the two major protein fractions, albumin and globulin, across the peritoneal membrane in the first few periods after labeled plasma injection (17).

The passage of at least *three times more albumin than globulin* across the barrier during the same period of time in terms of grams presumably is related to molecular qualities. From this difference in the rates of transfer, apparently similar in both directions, it is clear why the labeled globulin requires a longer time to reach or approximate equilibrium than does labeled albumin in these experiments. It is interesting to contrast this *slower rate of membrane passage of globulin* with its *metabolic turnover* in plasma which is appreciably more rapid than that of albumin (41).

DOG 50-5 – C^{14} PLASMA INTRAPERITONEALLY

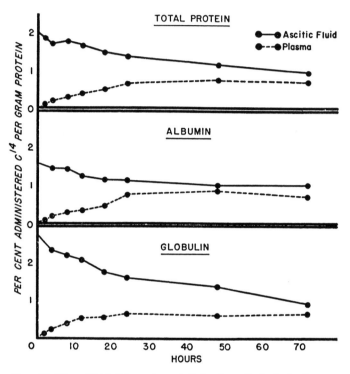

FIG. K. Dog 50-5—Experimental Ascites. Labeled plasma given intraperitoneally.

XXI
Red Blood Cell Stroma

IN THE ABUNDANT literature related to the red blood cell, one finds relatively few papers dealing with the *stroma residue*. Method difficulties are largely responsible. It is certain, however, that the stroma fraction is of the utmost importance, as it probably determines the life span of the red cell. The red blood cell presents many startling differences when compared with other cells of the human or animal body. These red cells start out with normal nuclei, and in this early stage, very little or no hemoglobin. We were told that the red cells extruded their nuclei, but in the rare instances where this is observed, it can safely be defined as an artefact. While the red cell shows nuclear changes resembling nuclear pyknosis and lysis, there is a rapid increase in the contained hemoglobin. It is hard to escape the belief that in some way the red cell nucleus contributes to the newly forming intracellular hemoglobin. The body metabolism meanwhile shows no evidence of nuclear destruction and elimination of nuclear end products during periods of active red cell production in severe experimental anemia due to blood loss in dogs.

When the red cell is worn out, the body conserves the end products to a remarkable degree. The iron is saved and promptly reutilized or stored (22). The globin fraction is also saved and used within the protein pool. If much hemoglobin appears in the plasma, some of it may escape by way of the kidney which has a definite threshold for hemoglobin. However, if the globin is given intraperitoneally, the dog can be kept in nitrogen equilibrium (25), all immediate needs of the body being met by utilization of this parenteral globin (22). The pigment fraction is largely discarded as the body apparently finds it easier to supply this radicle for new hemoglobin by synthesis. It is probable that the stroma residue is likewise conserved and reutilized in the body economy.

The *red blood cell* shows nuclear degeneration which in other body cells would mean death and prompt removal from organs or circulation. Yet the red cell in man or the dog lives a hectic life of about four months after this loss of its nucleus. The interrelationship of the stroma to the hemoglobin of the red cell is under active study in many laboratories, but no comprehensive statement can be made. However, it seems clear that the *formation of stroma precedes* that of the hemoglobin. The parent marrow cells contain no hemoglobin but large active-looking nuclei and present clean-cut cell outlines. Obviously stroma may be assumed to be present, and these cells are capable of very active growth and division.

This observation may be used in favor of a stroma which obviously is hemoglobin-free and to the effect that mature stroma is hemoglobin-free but for contamination and adsorption during analyses. As the daughter cells grow, they too show sharply defined cell contours and only traces of hemoglobin, so that it seems safe to conclude that the stroma and cell pattern are well-defined before recognizable hemoglobin appears.

How is the hemoglobin formed in the red cell? No hemoglobin can be detected in the plasma, even during the most active production of red cells in dogs subjected to continuous severe anemia where as much as 10 gm. hemoglobin is produced daily. It has been shown in this laboratory that plasma proteins can contribute something which is used by the maturing red cells to form hemoglobin (35). There is also some metabolic turnover related to hemoglobin in the mature red cells as measured by lysine containing radiocarbon.

XXII
Red Cell Stroma and Its Protein

THE STROMA RESIDUE contains a definite amount of protein which seems to be of importance as it is almost twice as abundant in the younger red cells found in severe anemia (Table 13). As the red cells age and the anemia decreases, this stroma protein decreases. A careful study of this stroma protein and comparison with hemoglobin and plasma proteins can be developed by the use of radiocarbon labeled lysine and other technics.

The *term red cell stroma* used in this paper covers the fraction designated in some papers as "red cell fixed framework," "ghosts," or "posthemolytic residue." The book, *Hemolysis and Related Phenomena*, by Eric Ponder should be consulted (24).

Method differences or errors in this field are noted. The methods defined will give values as indicated when identical samples of pooled blood are tested independently by various workers in this laboratory (31).

Red cell *stroma protein is increased in anemia* due to blood loss in the dog, on the average in severe anemia, almost twice the figures recorded in the pooled normal samples of red cell stroma (Table 13) (31). We wish to stress the importance

TABLE 13

COMPOSITION OF DOG STROMA IN ANEMIA
DUE TO BLOOD LOSS

Mg. Per Ml. R.B.C.	*Normal Average*	*Pooled Anemic Blood 6 Dogs*				*Individual Dogs, Anemic*		
		T	*C*	*R*	*Average*	*50-62*	*46-7*	*46-5*
Total protein	7.6	13.7	15.3	13.7	14.2	16.3	15.6	15.5
Hemoglobin	2.0	2.9	2.4	2.8	2.7	2.6	2.8	—
Total lipid	4.9	5.4	6.1	5.0	5.5	7.2	7.0	5.4
Total phospholipid	2.5	2.7	3.0	2.4	2.7	3.7	3.3	3.0
Hemoglobin blood level gm.	14.7				5.7	4.3	6.1	5.6

of the high protein fraction observed in anemic dog stroma. When completely understood, we will probably have a much better understanding of stroma and the durability of the mature red cell. If this protein concentration of the stroma can be modified by experiment, this knowledge may have some bearing on human anemias.

XXIII

The Eck Fistula Liver

THE LIVER IS the *master organ* for various *protein metabolic activities*—it makes proteins (fibrinogen, albumin, prothrombin, and probably other globulins), it stores proteins, and it aggregates amino acids and other materials coming from the gastrointestinal tract into new proteins. Whether these new-formed proteins may be liver proteins first and subsequently proteins for exchange and distribution (plasma proteins) is beside the point.

The normal liver having this key position in protein metabolism, observations made upon a liver which is somewhat abnormal will be of interest to students of physiology and pathology. The *Eck fistula liver* qualifies in this respect and as time and occasion permitted we have made observations on Eck fistula dogs, often maintained in an apparent state of health for as many as eight years. At times these dogs may present unusual disturbances of protein metabolism and again are close to normal. They may appear normal in all respects, activity, appetite, digestion and weight, but occasionally they may show increased thirst, diuresis, a trace of jaundice or lack of appetite, and vague intoxication. The fact that these dogs have tolerated an Eck fistula for from one to eight years speaks for a general state of good health (38).

The *Eck fistula* permits the portal blood to flow freely into the vena cava and excludes portal blood from the liver. The *blood supply* to this *liver is arterial* and probably but 25 to 35 per cent of normal. The Eck fistula liver is somewhat smaller than normal, but there is no significant fibrosis. The liver cells here and there may show fat droplets but for the most part appear normal. This liver may produce less bile salt than the normal control (29).

When the Eck fistula liver is put under the strain of producing blood proteins in an emergency (stimulus of anemia and hypoproteinemia), it is not surprising that it shows a lessened functional capacity as compared with the non-Eck control (Table 14). It *is* surprising that so often this Eck liver can approach the performance of the normal control. This may be attributed to the well-known reserve capacity of the liver.

The experiments above indicate that the liver is concerned directly or indirectly with the production of new hemoglobin. Our belief is that the liver contributes to the fabrication of hemoglobin by means of the mobile plasma proteins which to a large extent derive from the liver.

TABLE 14

ECK FISTULA DOG—ANEMIC AND HYPOPROTEINEMIC BLOOD
PROTEIN OUTPUT DECREASES SLOWLY

Period		Daily Diet	Protein Intake Average Per Week	Weight Average	Blood Levels Average		Protein Output Average Per Week	
No.	Duration				Hemo-globin	Plasma Protein	Hemo-globin	Plasma Protein
	wks.	gm.	gm.	kg.	gm. per cent	gm. per cent	gm.	gm.
1	7	Liver 150, basal	226	17.5	8.9	4.8	46.5	23.4
2	6	Liver 150, basal	226	16.8	8.7	4.9	40.1	19.6
3	4	Liver 150, basal	226	16.3	8.2	4.6	44.0	21.2
4	4	Liver 150, basal	226	16.3	6.9	4.6	33.8	18.1
5	10	Salmon 200, basal	277	18.3	7.1	5.0	15.7	9.0
6	5	Kidney 225, basal	269	18.9	7.4	5.2	34.8	19.9
7	2	Salmon 200, basal	277	18.5	7.0	5.1	11.5	7.1
8	6	Liver 200, basal	292	18.3	7.2	5.4	26.2	17.9
9	6	Salmon 200, basal	275	18.5	6.9	5.0	25.8	14.4
10	16	Salmon 200, basal	290	20.0	8.6	4.9	35.2	16.4
11	1	Salmon 200, basal	168	16.7	9.2	4.6	1.0	0
12	1	Salmon 150, liver 150	361	15.1	8.7	5.8	17.9	12.1
13	1	Salmon 100, liver 100, meat 150	435	15.7	7.0	6.3	44.6	28.9
14	2	Salmon 150, liver 225, basal	564	16.6	7.4	6.5	18.8	11.3

XXIV
Plasma Protein Synthesis in the Liver

T HE LIVER and *plasma protein synthesis* have been investigated recently by Miller, Bly, Watson and Bale (21) by means of the *perfused rat liver* and C^{14} lysine. They have mastered many of the difficulties inherent in organ perfusion. Their observations of the perfused liver are in harmony with the observations given above as recorded in the intact dog. The *perfused liver* is able to synthesize plasma proteins and to contribute these various proteins to the circulating blood plasma. This comprises albumin, fibrinogen and other globulins. In contrast, the *non-hepatic body tissues* when perfused are able to produce only small amounts of globulin but no fibrinogen and albumin (18, 20).

XXV

Ebb and Flow of Blood Proteins and the Related Stimuli

In THE NORMAL man or animal, the various blood proteins show minor fluctuations but in general are held in a steady state or equilibrium between wear and tear or general use and new regeneration. *Various stimuli* may affect production of blood proteins, but often more than one stimulus is involved and one cannot be sure as to the mechanism. For example, change in oxygen tension will modify the formation of red cells and hemoglobin. Living at high altitude will stimulate the formation of new red cells and a higher count of red cells is recorded. It is to be noted that in the normal dog (36) it takes about 3 to 5 days for the red cells to be formed in the bone marrow and appear in the general circulation. These red cells then continue their function for approximately 120 days (33) in the dog. Other stimuli react on the marrow red cell producing units—for example, food or amino acid deficiencies (5).

The stimuli responsible for *production of plasma proteins* are largely unknown. *Fibrinogen* is the most labile of the plasma proteins and certainly derives from the liver. Inflammation increases its production and rapidity of turnover.

Its concentration in the plasma may rise from normal 0.3-0.4 gm. per cent to 0.8-1.1 gm. per cent with multiple abscesses, pneumonia, etc. (14). Liver injury causes a drop in the fibrinogen levels but a simultaneous abscess may stimulate the injured liver to increase fibrinogen production—a *relative* increase—a combined effect of injury of liver and inflammation giving a fibrinogen level perhaps not far from the normal level. It is reasonable to assume that materials derived from the inflamed and injured area do act as stimuli to accelerate fibrinogen production (39).

Albumin presents a different picture. It represents the greatest mass of plasma proteins and is produced in the liver. We believe it has much to do with the *"protein climate" of the organ cells.* It passes readily into organ or tissue cells when no protein is fed and plasma protein is given by vein. It then must be concerned with *intracellular metabolism*—the animal remains normal for months and is in positive nitrogen equilibrium. What stimulus is responsible for albumin production? Probably multiple stimuli increase albumin output—for example, hypoproteinemia and changes in osmotic pressure. Other conditions may be responsible for hypoalbumenemia and inhibition of albumin production—for example, overproduction of various globulins associated with disease.

Globulins are numerous and many of them relate to the liver, but others are produced at least in part outside of the liver. Fibrinogen has been mentioned and other globulins concerned with blood coagulation also derive from the liver. The antibody globulins have been much studied and may react to specific stimuli. The stimuli related to the blood coagulation globulins are probably multiple and certainly are not known. The fact that in emergencies these various globulins can be used to maintain nitrogen balance of organ and tissue cells makes the interpretation of fluctuations in the concentration of these plasma proteins all the more difficult.

Observations on *globulins in clinical disease* add much to our understanding of these plasma proteins. Some patients are observed who from birth lack one or more of these globulins (e.g., fibinogen and other coagulation factors). Study of such cases adds much to our knowledge but does not simplify the equation as presently understood.

Antibody proteins have been investigated during recent years and probably more work has been done with these plasma globulins by means of the antibody reactions than by the isotope methods. Much of this work was reviewed recently at a symposium and has been published (23).

Figure L is an attempt to picture the *ebb and flow or dynamic equilibrium* of the common blood, lymph, organ and tissue proteins. Obviously many details cannot be included as the complexity of

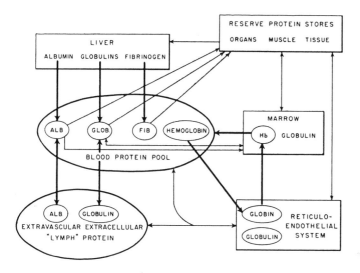

DYNAMIC EQUILIBRIUM OF BODY PROTEINS

FIG. L. Dynamic equilibrium of body proteins.

the figure would then defeat its purpose—to visualize the main features of this reaction. Albumin and globulins are *"messenger proteins"* in the sense that they can be contributed to the blood protein pool and thereby to the cells of the bone marrow, various organs and reticulo-endothelial system. These messenger proteins can sustain all protein requirements of organ cell protein metabolism.

The *Hemoglobin cycle* (marrow→circulation→ reticulo-endothelial system→circulation→marrow) is a tight little cycle to which the blood plasma proteins surely add some needed material. The *reserve stores* in various organs and tissues present many important and fascinating problems. The stores are protein material but probably not the same protein if one examines and compares these stores in the liver, muscle and marrow. The shift from one reserve to another can be demonstrated and it takes place readily under favorable conditions. Surely the protein passes into and out of a given cell without extensive cleavage to the amino acid level—yet presumably the protein character varies in these organ stores.

Bibliography

1. BEST, C. H., and TAYLOR, N. B.: *Physiological Basis of Medical Practice*. Baltimore, Williams & Wilkins, 1943, p. 1022.
2. BIKENBACK, W., and RUPP, H.: *Ztschr. Geburtsh. u. Gynak.*, *103*:170, 183, 1932.
3. BLOCK, R. J., and BOLLING, D.: *Arch. Biochem.*, *3*:217, 1943.
4. BRAMBELL, F. W. R., HEMMINGS, W. A., HENDERSON, M., PARRY, H. J., and ROWLANDS, W. T.: *Proc. Roy. Soc. London* (Series B), *136*:131, 1949.
5. CANNON, P. R.: Protein and Amino Acid Deficiencies. *Am. Lectures in Pathol.*, 1948.
6. DAFT, F. S., ROBSCHEIT-ROBBINS, F .S., and WHIPPLE, G. H.: *J. Biol. Chem.*, *121*:45, 1937.
7. FOSTER, D. P., and WHIPPLE, G. H.: *Am. J. Physiol.*, *58*:365, 407, 1922.
8. HAHN, P. F., BALE, W. F., ROSS, J. F., BALFOUR, W. M., and WHIPPLE, G. H.: *J. Exper. Med.*, *78*:169, 1943.
9. HOWE, P. E., and HAWK, P. B.: *J. Am. Chem. Soc.*, *33*:215, 1911.
10. HOWE, P. E., MATTILL, H. A., and HAWK, P. B.: *J. Biol. Chem.*, *11*:103, 1912.
11. HOWLAND, J. W., and HAWKINS, W. B.: *J. Biol. Chem.*, *123*:99, 1938.
12. KELLNER, A., and HEDAL, E. F.: *J. Exper. Med.*, *97*:51, 1953.
13. MADDEN, S. C., and CLAY, W. A.: *J. Exper. Med.*, *82*:65, 1945.

14. Madden, S. C., and Whipple, G. H.: *Physiol. Rev.*, 20:194, 1940.

15. McKee, F. W., Schloerb, P. R., Schilling, J. A., Tishkoff, G. H., and Whipple, G. H.: *J. Exper. Med.*, 87:457, 1948.

16. McKee, F. W., Wilt, W. G., Hyatt, R. E., and Whipple, G. H.: *J. Exper. Med.*, 91:115, 1950.

17. McKee, F. W., Yuile, C. L., Lamson, B. G., and Whipple, G. H.: *J. Exper. Med.*, 95:161, 1952.

18. Miller, L. L., and Bale, W. F.: *J. Exper. Med.*, 99:125, 1954.

19. Miller, L. L., Bale, W. F., Yuile, C. L., Masters, R. E., Tishkoff, G. H., and Whipple, G. H.: *J. Exper. Med.*, 90:297, 1949.

20. Miller, L. L., Bly, C. G., and Bale, W. F.: *J. Exper. Med.*, 99:133, 1954.

21. Miller, L. L., Bly, C. G., Watson, M. L., and Bale, W. F.: *J. Exper. Med.*, 94:431, 1951.

22. Miller, L. L., Robscheit-Robbins, F. S., and Whipple, G. H.: *J. Exper. Med.*, 81:405, 1945.

23. Pappenheimer, A. M.: *Nature and Significance of Antibody Response*, New York, Columbia Univ. Press, 1953.

24. Ponder, E.: *Hemolysis and Related Phenomena*, New York, Grune & Stratton, 1948.

25. Robscheit-Robbins, F. S., and Miller, L. L.: *Ann. New York Acad. Sc.*, 47:317, 1946.

26. Robscheit-Robbins, F. S., and Whipple, G .H.: *J. Exper. Med.*, 63:767, 1936.

27. Robscheit-Robbins, F. S., and Whipple, G. H.: *J. Exper. Med.*, 63:767, 774, 1936.

28. SCHOENHEIMER, R., RATNER, S., RITENBURG, D., and HEIDELBERGER, M.: *J. Biol. Chem.*, *144*: 545, 1942.

29. SMITH, H. P., and WHIPPLE, G. H.: *J. Biol Chem.*, 89:739, 1930.

30. TERRY, R., SANDROCK, W., NYE, R., and WHIPPLE, G. H.: *J. Exper. Med.*, 87:547, 1948.

31. TISHKOFF, G. H., ROBSCHEIT-ROBBINS, F. S., and WHIPPLE, G. H.: *Blood*, 8:459, 1953.

32. WHIPPLE, G. H.: *Am. J. Med. Sc.*, 203:477, 1942.

33. WHIPPLE, G. H., BALE, W. F., YUILE, C. L., DeLaVERGNE, L., and MILLER, L. L.: *J. Exper. Med.*, 90:315, 1949.

34. WHIPPLE, G. H., HILL, R. B., JR., TERRY, R., LUCAS, F. V., and YUILE, C. L.: *J. Exper. Med.*, 101:617, 1955.

35. WHIPPLE, G. H., and MADDEN, S. C.: *Medicine*, 23:215, 1944.

36. WHIPPLE, G. H., MILLER, L. L., BALE, W. F., YUILE, C. L., MASTERS, R. E., and TISHKOFF, G. H.: *J. Exper. Med.*, 90:297, 1949.

37. WHIPPLE, G. H., MILLER, L. L., and ROBSCHEIT-ROBBINS, F. S.: *J. Exper. Med.*, 85:277, 1947.

38. WHIPPLE, G. H., ROBSCHEIT-ROBBINS, F. S., and HAWKINS, W. B.: *J. Exper. Med.*, 81:171, 1945.

39. WHIPPLE, G. H., YUILE, C. L., LUCAS, F. V., JONES, C. K., and CHAPIN, S. J.: *J. Exper. Med.*, 98:173, 1953.

40. WISLOCKI, G. B., DEMPSEY, E. W., and FAWCETT, D. W.: *Obst. & Gynec. Surv.*, 3:604, 1948.

41. YUILE, C. L., LAMSON, B. G., MILLER, L. L., and WHIPPLE, G. H.: *J. Exper. Med.*, 93:539, 1951.

42. YUILE, C. L., LUCAS, F. V., JONES, C. K., CHAPIN, S. J., and WHIPPLE, G. H.: *J. Exper. Med.*, 98: 1, 1953.
43. YUILE, C. L., O'DEA, A. E., LUCAS, F. V., and WHIPPLE, G. H.: *J. Exper. Med.*, 96:247, 1952.

This Book

THE DYNAMIC EQUILIBRIUM
OF BODY PROTEINS

By

GEORGE H. WHIPPLE, M.D.

was set, printed and bound by The Collegiate Press of Menasha, Wisconsin. The engravings were made by the Northwestern Engraving Company of Menasha, Wisconsin. The page trim size is 5½ x 8½ inches. The type page is 21 x 37 picas. The type face is Linotype Caledonia, and Bodoni Bold set 12 point on 14 point. The text paper is 70 lb. White Winnebago Eggshell.

With THOMAS BOOKS *careful attention is given to all details of manufacturing and design. It is the Publisher's desire to present books that are satisfactory as to their physical qualities and artistic possibilities and appropriate for their particular use.* THOMAS BOOKS *will be true to those laws of quality that assure a good name and good will.*